GOSCINNY AND UDERZO

PRESENT

An Asterix Adventure

ASTERIX AND OBELIX ALL AT SEA

Written and Illustrated by ALBERT UDERZO

Translated by ANTHEA BELL *and* DEREK HOCKRIDGE

To my grandson, Thomas,
and in homage to that great actor,
Kirk Douglas

Original edition © 1996 Les Éditions Albert René / Goscinny-Uderzo
English translation © 1996 Les Éditions Albert René / Goscinny-Uderzo
Original title: *La Galère d'Obélix*

Exclusive licensee: Orion Publishing Group
Translators: Anthea Bell and Derek Hockridge
Typography: Bryony Newhouse

This paperback edition first published in 2002 by Orion Books Ltd,
Orion House, 5 Upper Saint Martin's Lane, London WC2H 9EA

7 9 10 8 6

Printed in France by Partenaires

http://gb.asterix.com
www.orionbooks.co.uk

A CIP record for this book is available from the British Library

ISBN-13 978 0 75284 717 7 (cased)
ISBN-10 0 75284 717 1 (cased)
ISBN-13 978 0 75284 778 8 (paperback)
ISBN-10 0 75284 778 3 (paperback)

Distributed in the United States of America by Sterling Publishing Co. Inc.
387 Park Avenue South, New York, NY 10016

GAULISH VILLAGE

COMPENDIUM

LAUDANUM

AQUARIUM

TOTORUM

ARMORICA

BELGICA

LUTETIA

GAUL
(ROMAN CONQUEST)
50 BC

CELTICA

AQUITANIA

PROVINCIA

THE YEAR IS 50 BC. GAUL IS ENTIRELY OCCUPIED BY THE
ROMANS. WELL, NOT ENTIRELY . . . ONE SMALL VILLAGE OF
THE INDOMITABLE GAULS STILL HOLDS OUT AGAINST THE
INVADERS. AND LIFE IS NOT EASY FOR THE ROMAN LEGION-
ARIES WHO GARRISON THE FORTIFIED CAMPS OF TOTORUM,
AQUARIUM, LAUDANUM AND COMPENDIUM . . .

ASTERIX, THE HERO OF THESE ADVENTURES. A SHREWD, CUNNING LITTLE WARRIOR, ALL PERILOUS MISSIONS ARE IMMEDIATELY ENTRUSTED TO HIM. ASTERIX GETS HIS SUPERHUMAN STRENGTH FROM THE MAGIC POTION BREWED BY THE DRUID GETAFIX . . .

OBELIX, ASTERIX'S INSEPARABLE FRIEND. A MENHIR DELIVERY-MAN BY TRADE, ADDICTED TO WILD BOAR. OBELIX IS ALWAYS READY TO DROP EVERYTHING AND GO OFF ON A NEW ADVENTURE WITH ASTERIX − SO LONG AS THERE'S WILD BOAR TO EAT, AND PLENTY OF FIGHTING. HIS CONSTANT COMPANION IS DOGMATIX, THE ONLY KNOWN CANINE ECOLOGIST, WHO HOWLS WITH DESPAIR WHEN A TREE IS CUT DOWN.

GETAFIX, THE VENERABLE VILLAGE DRUID, GATHERS MISTLETOE AND BREWS MAGIC POTIONS. HIS SPECIALITY IS THE POTION WHICH GIVES THE DRINKER SUPERHUMAN STRENGTH. BUT GETAFIX ALSO HAS OTHER RECIPES UP HIS SLEEVE . . .

FINALLY, VITALSTATISTIX, THE CHIEF OF THE TRIBE. MAJESTIC, BRAVE AND HOT-TEMPERED, THE OLD WARRIOR IS RESPECTED BY HIS MEN AND FEARED BY HIS ENEMIES. VITALSTATISTIX HIMSELF HAS ONLY ONE FEAR, HE IS AFRAID THE SKY MAY FALL ON HIS HEAD TOMORROW. BUT AS HE ALWAYS SAYS, TOMORROW NEVER COMES.

CACOFONIX, THE BARD. OPINION IS DIVIDED AS TO HIS MUSICAL GIFTS. CACOFONIX THINKS HE'S A GENIUS. EVERY-ONE ELSE THINKS HE'S UNSPEAKABLE. BUT SO LONG AS HE DOESN'T SPEAK, LET ALONE SING, EVERYBODY LIKES HIM . . .

5

* STRAITS OF GIBRALTAR.

* SEE ASTERIX IN BRITAIN

LATER, SOME WAY OFF IN GAUL...

I HAD A TERRIBLE NIGHTMARE LAST NIGHT, ASTERIX!

YOU DID?

I DREAMED THAT JULIUS CAESAR DECIDED TO WITHDRAW ALL THE GARRISONS SURROUNDING THE VILLAGE!

JUST A TOUCH OF INDIGESTION, OBELIX! I KEEP TELLING YOU NOT TO EAT MORE THAN THREE BOARS BEFORE GOING TO BED!

BUT I CAN'T GET TO SLEEP WITHOUT AT LEAST FOUR INSIDE ME!

WELL, IT WAS ONLY A NIGHTMARE! AND EVEN IF YOUR DREAM CAME TRUE...

WHAT DO YOU MEAN, CAME TRUE?!

WHY NOT? WE MIGHT FINALLY GET PEACE WITH HONOUR!

COME ALONG, DOGMATIX! WE WANT NOTHING TO DO WITH THESE POLICIES OF APPEASEMENT!

?!

OH, OBELIX, DON'T BE SO SILLY! I WAS ONLY JOKING!

OH NO, YOU WEREN'T, MISTER ASTERIX!

YOU WERE INSULTING THE MEMORY OF VERCINGETORIX! HAVE YOU GONE COMPLETELY BONKERS?

RAISE THE ALARM!! THE ROMANS ARE ABOUT TO ATTACK!!

!!!

A GOOD THING THE ROMANS HAVE GOT MORE SENSE THAN YOU, MISTER ASTERIX!

THAT'S FUNNY! THERE WAS NOTHING TO SUGGEST THEY WERE GOING TO ATTACK!

9

I SAW THEM! THE GARRISONS OF ALL FOUR FORTIFIED CAMPS ARE DRAWN UP ON THE OTHER SIDE OF THE FOREST!

!!?

HMMM..

RIGHT! WE MUST BE PREPARED! CAN YOU DOLE OUT THE MAGIC POTION, GETAFIX?

I MADE TWO CAULDRONS JUST IN CASE, ALTHOUGH ONE IS PLENTY!

HURRY UP! NEXT!

THE EFFECTS OF THE POTION NEVER CEASE TO AMAZE ME!

SOMETHING WRONG, OBELIX?

POOR OLD OBELIX! I EXPECT GETAFIX WOULDN'T GIVE HIM ANY MAGIC POTION, AS USUAL!

WE KNOW IT HAD A PERMANENT EFFECT ON HIM... BUT WHAT WOULD HAPPEN IF HE DRANK SOME MORE NOW?

THERE'D BE DANGEROUS SIDE EFFECTS, ASTERIX, AND ALL MY SKILL WOULD BE POWERLESS TO COUNTERACT THEM!

SOON AFTERWARDS...

THIS IS ODD, O DRUID! OBELIX IS MISSING!

YOU KNOW HOW TOUCHY HE IS! HE MUST HAVE GONE OFF IN A SULK, BUT I'M SURE HE'LL BE THE FIRST TO GO FOR THE ROMANS.

14

NIGHT HAS FALLEN ON THE LITTLE VILLAGE. EVERYONE IS DEEPLY UPSET BY THE INCIDENT. LIGHT SHOWS IN ONLY TWO HUTS...

ONE IS THE HOME OF THE DRUID, WHO IS NOT VERY HOPEFULLY BREWING A POTION WHICH HE ALONE KNOWS THE SECRET...

AND THE OTHER IS POOR OBELIX'S HOUSE. HIS FRIEND ASTERIX IS STILL SITTING UP WITH HIM.

IN THE SMALL HOURS...

HAS HE MOVED AT ALL?

I'M AFRAID NOT.

NOW TO WAIT FOR THE POTION TO TAKE EFFECT... AND HOPE!

AREN'T YOU SURE IT WILL WORK, THEN?

I'VE NEVER HAD A CASE LIKE THIS BEFORE... BUT WE MUST LEAVE NO STONE UNTURNED!

WOOF!

YOU'RE THE BEST DRUID IN THE UNIVERSE, GETAFIX! DOGMATIX AND I ARE SURE YOU'LL MANAGE TO CURE OBELIX!

MAY TOUTATIS HEAR YOU, ASTERIX! MAY TOUTATIS HEAR YOU!

15

HERE'S THE ADMIRAL, VICE-ADMIRAL!

ANOTHER OF THE TOP BRASS!

YOU CALL THESE ROMANS? GONE INTO A DECLINE ALREADY, HAVE THEY???

ER... WELL, THE FACT IS...

THE FACT IS WHAT, NAUTILUS?

WELL, YOU SEE, WE WERE JUST PEACEFULLY PARADING...

...WHEN ALL OF A SUDDEN...

ARE YOU SAYING THAT HANDFUL OF GAULS DID THIS TO YOU?

WELL, THEY ARE A HANDFUL... I WAS MUCH STRUCK BY IT MYSELF, ADMIRAL!

NEVER MIND! FOLLOW ME. I HAVE TO TALK TO YOU.

WELL, ADMIRAL CRUSTACIUS, CAN YOU TELL ME WHAT WE'RE DOING IN THIS JUPITER-FORSAKEN COUNTRY?

OUR FLEET IS FOLLOWING CAESAR'S GALLEY AT A DISTANCE. IT IS NOW APPROACHING THE COAST OF ARMOR- ICA, AND OBVIOUSLY THE MUTINEERS WILL TRY TO TAKE REFUGE IN THE VILLAGE OF INDOMITABLE GAULS!

I GET IT! AS SOON AS THEY DISEMBARK AND LEAVE THE SHIP, WE GRAB IT BACK! BRILLIANT IDEA!!!

HO, HO, HO! AND I'LL SOON PERSUADE THE GAULS TO HAND THOSE MUTINEERS OVER!

ER... THAT MIGHT NOT BE SUCH A BRIL- LIANT IDEA!

17

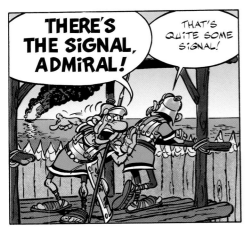

19

23

THAT ONE OUGHT TO DO!

OBELIX QUARRY

GNNNNNNNNN

GNNNNNNNNN

BOOHOOHOO!

I DID SO WANT TO GIVE PANACEA THIS LOVELY PRESENT!

YOU SEE, DOGMATIX, I'M NOT THE MAN I WAS! I CAN'T EAT THREE MEASLY LITTLE BOARS OR LIFT THE TINIEST LITTLE MENHIR!

WELL, I KNOW WHAT I MUST DO... GO AND LIVE IN THE FOREST ALL BY MYSELF! YOU CAN COME TOO IF YOU LIKE, DOGMATIX!

OBELIX QUARRY

O GETAFIX, I HAVEN'T SEEN OBELIX FOR HOURS! I'M AFRAID HE MAY BE UP TO SOMETHING SILLY AGAIN!

WELL, AT LEAST HE CAN'T BE DRINKING ANY MORE MAGIC POTION. I'M RIGHT OUT OF STOCK!

BUT WHO KNOWS... THE POTION MIGHT GET HIM BACK TO NORMAL!

I WON'T TAKE THE RISK! OBELIX HAS SUFFERED TOO MANY SEA CHANGES FOR ME TO SEE HIM CHANGE ANY MORE!

MEANWHILE...

THE ADMIRAL'S GETTING ON MY NERVES, INSISTING ON FINDING GAULISH HOSTAGES! I KNOW ONLY TOO WELL WHAT WILL HAPPEN IF WE FIND A SINGLE ONE!

DOGMATIX IS BEHAVING ODDLY! THAT MEANS OBELIX MUST BE IN DANGER!!!!

WOOF! WOOF!

YOU WAIT HERE, DOGMATIX. I MUST TELL THE OTHERS!

OBELIX IS IN DANGER!! I'M OFF TO HELP HIM!

THIS MUST BE THE ROMANS' DOING! WE'LL BE WITH YOU, ASTERIX!

WAIT WHILE I MAKE ANOTHER CAULDRON OF POTION! I THINK YOU'RE GOING TO NEED SOME MORE!

SOON AFTERWARDS...

YOU WILL BE AMONG THE FEW VISITORS TO OUR VILLAGE EVER TO HAVE DRUNK THE MAGIC POTION!

IT'S A GREAT HONOUR FOR US, O VENERABLE DRUID!

AND FINALLY...

DOGMATIX WILL LEAD US STRAIGHT TO OBELIX'S KIDNAPPERS!

SNIFF! SNIFF! SNIFF!

I KNEW IT! THAT'S WHERE OBELIX IS BEING HELD PRISONER!

26

SURE ENOUGH, THE ADMIRAL'S SHIP, ALL SAILS SET, IS MAKING FOR OSTIA, THE PORT OF ROME, WITH A POOR LITTLE GAUL BELOW DECKS AND FEELING VERY LOW...

SO I GO BACK TO CHILDHOOD! SO I LOSE MY STRENGTH! THE ROMANS AREN'T AFRAID OF ME ANY MORE AND I'M THEIR PRISONER...

OH ASTERIX, PLEASE COME AND HELP ME OUT OF THIS!

WHAT ARE WE WAITING FOR? WE MUST CATCH UP WITH THE ROMAN SHIP AND RESCUE OBELIX!

MY CREW AND I ARE READY TO PURSUE THE ADMIRAL'S GALLEY, ASTERIX!

I'LL COME WITH YOU. I'VE JUST HAD AN IDEA WHICH MIGHT SOLVE POOR OBELIX'S PROBLEMS!

?!

HERE'S YOUR GOURD OF POTION, ASTERIX! I'VE FILLED THIS BARREL TOO, BECAUSE I WON'T BE ABLE TO BREW ANY MORE ON THE VOYAGE!

WE'LL KEEP IT AWAY FROM THE BARRELS OF DRINKING WATER, TO BE ON THE SAFE SIDE!

AND SOON AFTERWARDS...

WE'LL SOON OVERTAKE THE ADMIRAL'S SHIP, THANKS TO THE EFFECTS OF YOUR POTION, O DRUID!

YES, AND ONCE WE'VE RESCUED OBELIX I'LL TELL YOU MY IDEA, ASTERIX!

FLOP! FLOP! FLOP! FLOP!

THE ADMIRAL'S GALLEY CAPTURED BY THE GAULS IS GOING IN THE OPPOSITE DIRECTION FROM THE GALLEY NOW BEING SAILED BY THE PIRATES.

YOU SAID YOU HAD AN IDEA FOR HELPING OBELIX, O DRUID!

THAT'S RIGHT! IT'S TIME TO TAKE AN IMPORTANT DECISION, ASTERIX!

SPARTAKIS, I BELIEVE YOU'RE A GOOD SAILOR?

SO DO I! I'M GREEK, YOU KNOW!

WOULD YOU AND YOUR CREW AGREE TO TAKE US TO A DISTANT ISLAND?

WHAT'S THIS DISTANT ISLAND CALLED?

ATLANTIS!

?!

?

I THOUGHT THAT LEGENDARY CONTINENT SANK BENEATH THE WAVES LONG AGO!

IT DID. BUT A GROUP OF OFF-SHORE ISLANDS WAS LEFT.* THE LARGEST IS STILL INHABITED BY THE LAST ATLANTEANS!

* SOMETIMES THOUGHT TO BE THE CANARY ISLANDS.

BUT WHAT DOES THIS ATLANTIS PLACE HAVE TO DO WITH OBELIX?

THE ATLANTEANS ARE DESCENDED FROM A VERY ANCIENT CIVILIZATION, FAR MORE ADVANCED THAN OUR OWN. OBELIX COULD BENEFIT FROM THEIR SKILLS!

WE AGREE, DRUID! WE'LL SET COURSE FOR ATLANTIS! ER... THE CREW WOULDN'T MIND BENEFITING FROM YOUR POTION AGAIN.

OF COURSE!

I'LL FETCH SOME FROM THE RESERVE BARREL!

AND THIS LAST BARREL IS FULL OF WATER TOO... BUT THEN... *THAT MUST MEAN...*

GETAFIX! WE'VE GOT NO MORE MAGIC POTION!

AND THIS TIME YOU CAN'T BLAME ME!

FOLLOW ME, FRIENDS! COME AND HAVE A LITTLE REST AND REFRESHMENT!

HEY, GETAFIX, LOOK AT THAT! A FLYING COW!!!

WELL, THEY NEED MILK FOR ALL THESE CHILDREN, ASTERIX!

HOW IS IT THAT EXCEPT FOR YOU, HIGH PRIEST, ATLANTIS SEEMS TO BE ENTIRELY INHABITED BY CHILDREN?

ALL THOSE CHILDREN WERE ONCE ADULTS WHO WANTED TO GO BACK TO CHILDHOOD!

YES, I KNOW, THESE ADULTS ARE CR...

IF ONLY THEY AT LEAST HAD FLYING WILD BOAR!!!

GO BACK TO CHILDHOOD? HOW COULD THEY POSSIBLY DO THAT?

OVER MANY CENTURIES THE ATLANTEANS LEARNED AMONG OTHER THINGS, THE SECRET OF REJUVENATION AND ETERNAL YOUTH.

THE SKILLS OF THE ATLANTEANS ARE THE SOLE REASON FOR OUR VOYAGE!

YOU MEAN YOU WANT TO GO BACK TO CHILDHOOD TOO?

NO, QUITE THE OPPOSITE! OBELIX HERE LOST HIS ADULT APPEARANCE BY ACCIDENT. CAN YOU GIVE IT BACK TO HIM?

HE WANTS TO GROW OLDER? THAT'S FUNNY...

UNFORTUNATELY, I KNOW THE SECRET OF THE ELIXIR OF YOUTH BUT NOT THE ELIXIR OF AGE. I'M AFRAID I CAN'T HELP YOUR FRIEND!

OH DEAR! SO WE CAME ALL THIS WAY FOR NOTHING! WE'LL JUST HAVE TO GO HOME TO OUR VILLAGE!

ALL THE SAME, HIGH PRIEST, I MUST SAY I THINK YOUR SKILLS ARE ABSOLUTELY FABULOUS TOO!

I'M ONLY SORRY THEY'RE NO HELP TO YOU!

SOMETIMES I ENVY OUR FRIEND OBELIX! HE DOESN'T KNOW HOW LUCKY HE IS, GETTING HIS CHILDHOOD BACK! WELL, WE'D BETTER BE OFF, THE CREW WILL BE WAITING.

ER... THE FACT IS...

...IF THE HIGH PRIEST AGREES, THE CREW AND I WOULD LIKE TO STAY. ATLANTIS SEEMS TO BE A LAND OF LIBERTY!

!?

?!

VERY WELL, STRICTLY ON CONDITION THAT OUR GAULISH FRIENDS NEVER REVEAL THE EXISTENCE OF ATLANTIS!

WE SWEAR NEVER TO MENTION IT, ABSOLUTLI-FABULOS!

I'M SURE YOU UNDERSTAND, ASTERIX!

OF COURSE! YOU'LL BE REALLY FREE MEN HERE!

I SAY, OLD BOY, WE HAD SOME GOOD TIMES, WHAT?

IT WAS NICE MEETING A LITTLE BUNDLE OF JOY LIKE YOU... AND YOUR SEA-DOG THERE!

CAN WE ASK YOU ONE MORE FAVOUR HIGH PRIEST?

SO NOW WE CAN ONLY RELY ON THE KINDNESS OF AEOLUS* TO GET US HOME.

I THINK I CAN GUESS WHAT IT IS!

I FEAR SO.

*GOD OF THE WINDS.

THE INGREDIENTS FOR THE MAGIC POTION AREN'T AVAILABLE ON THIS ISLAND!

WELL, WE STILL HAVE THE CONTENTS OF MY GOURD IF NECESSARY!

IT'S A SHAME YOU'RE GOING! WE HAVE A GREAT TIME HERE!

FAR FROM CAESAR'S GALLEY...

ROMAN GALLEY MAKING RIGHT FOR US!

ADMIRAL'S GALLEY RIGHT AHEAD!

THAT'S ODD, I THOUGHT IT WAS MAKING FOR ROME?

WE CAN'T AVOID THEM WITHOUT OARSMEN, ASTERIX!

I STILL HAVE MY GOURD OF MAGIC POTION, REMEMBER?

IT'S THE GAULS!

?!?

THIS IS ODD... LET'S PLAY SAFE AND SEND A WARNING SHOT ACROSS THEIR BOWS BEFORE WE BOARD THEM!

I'M COVERING YOU! DON'T BE AFRAID!

WHO'S AFRAID OF ANYONE?

BE CAREFUL, ASTERIX! I HAVE A NASTY FOREBODING!

GRRRRR!

PAF!

SPLASH

PFFF!

SURRENDER, GAULS!

WHAT HAVE YOU DONE WITH THE ADMIRAL AND HIS CREW? WHO ARE YOU?

YOU'LL SOON FIND OUT IF YOU TOUCH ANOTHER HAIR OF MY FRIEND ASTERIX'S HEAD!

GRRR!

PHEW! I FINALLY MANAGED TO SALVAGE THIS GOURD OF...

OBELIX!!! WHAT HAPPENED?

NO IDEA. IT COULD HAVE BEEN THE EFFECT OF SEEING ASTERIX IN DANGER. BUT WHO DID THAT TO YOU... THE ROMANS?

NO, THE SHARKS. BUT I TOOK A MOUTHFUL OF POTION AND THEY DIDN'T PUT THE BITE ON ME!

ASTERIX LOOKS IN BAD SHAPE.

OH. HE'LL SOON BE FINE! A POTION A DAY KEEPS THE ROMANS AWAY!

GLUG! GLUG! GLUG!

?!

OBELIX!!! WHAT HAPPENED?

YES. I KNOW THIS IS GETTING REPETITIVE, BUT IT'S A QUESTION WORTH ASKING!

GOOD THING I BROUGHT YOUR CLOTHES ALONG JUST IN CASE!

YOU'RE THE BEST FRIEND I KNOW, ASTERIX!

AAAAH! IT'S GOOD TO GET BACK TO MY OWN SIZE!

AND IT'LL BE GOOD TO GET HOME! HIGH TIME WE WENT BACK TO THE VILLAGE!

DOGMATIX AND I WILL ROW!

YIPPEE!!

MEANWHILE, FAR AWAY...

THE ADMIRAL'S BEEN DOWN THERE AN AWFULLY LONG TIME! I'D BETTER TAKE A LOOK!

?!

47

THE END

— UDERZO — 96